Wise Publications
part of The Music Sales Group
London / New York / Paris / Sydney / Copenhagen / Berlin / Madrid / Hong Kong / Tokyo

Published by
Wise Publications
14-15 Berners Street, London W1T 3LJ, UK.

Exclusive distributors:
Music Sales Limited
Distribution Centre,
Newmarket Road, Bury St Edmunds, Suffolk, IP33 3YB, UK.
Music Sales Pty Limited
20 Resolution Drive, Caringbah, NSW 2229, Australia.

Order No. AM1000868
ISBN 978-1-84938-589-3

Edited by Jenni Wheeler.

Printed in the EU.

Alone

Words & Music by Billy Steinberg & Tom Kelly

Bust A Move

Words & Music by Matt Dike, Marvin Young, Michael Ross,
Jim Walters & Luther Rabb

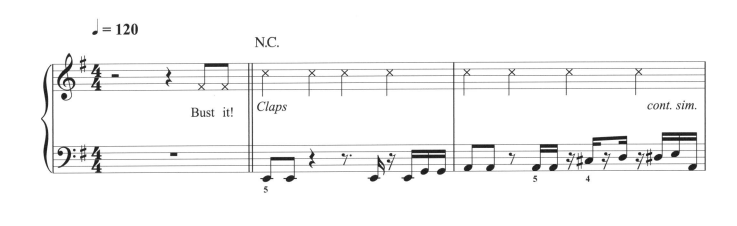

girl starts walk - in', guys start gawk - in', sits down next to you___ and starts talk - in'.
dressed in yel - low, she says "hel - lo, come sit next to me___ you fine fel - low." You

To Coda II

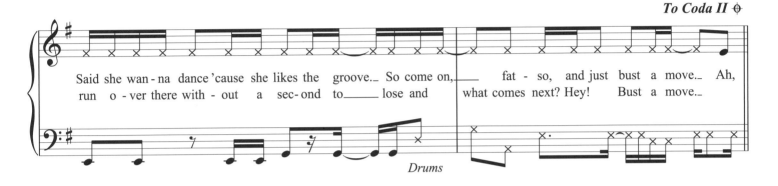

Said she wan - na dance 'cause she likes the groove.___ So come on,___ fat - so, and just bust a move.___ Ah,
run o - ver there with - out a sec - ond to___ lose and what comes next? Hey! Bust a move.___

Drums

1.

hey, yeah, ah. Ah, hey, yeah.

(Just bust a move!)___ Ah,___ hey. Ah,___ yeah. Ah,

hey, yeah, ah. 2. You're

Coda II

You＿want it, you got it. Ah. You＿ want it, ba-

1.
- by you got it. Ah.
(Just bust a move.)

2.
N.C.
- by you got it. Ah,＿ ah,＿ ah,＿

5

＿ hey.＿ Ah,＿ hah,＿ yeah,＿ ah.＿ Hah,＿ hey,＿ hah,＿

5 4 5 4

＿ hey.＿ Ah, hah,＿ hey,＿ yeah,＿ yeah.＿

Verse 3:
Your best friend Harry has a brother Larry
In five days from now he's gonna marry
He's hopin' you can make it there if you can
'Cause in the ceremony you'll be the best man.

You say "neato", check your libido
And roll to the church in your new tuxedo
The bride walks down just to start the wedding
And there's one more girl you won't be getting.

So you start thinkin', then you start blinkin'
A bride maid looks and thinks that you're winkin'
She thinks you're kinda cute so she winks back
And then you're feelin' really fine 'cause the girl is stacked.

Reception's jumpin, bass in pumpin'
Look at the girl, and your heart starts thumpin'
Says she wants to dance to a different groove
Now you know what to do, G, bust a move.

13

Can't Fight This Feeling

Words & Music by Kevin Cronin

16

Dancing With Myself

Words & Music by Billy Idol & Tony James

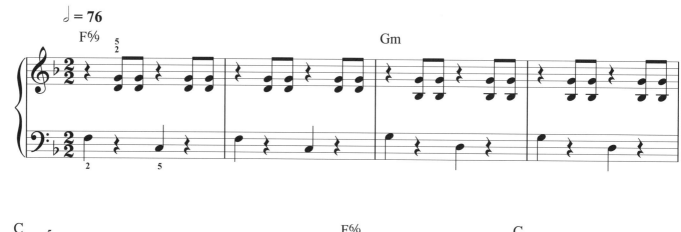

floors of To-ky-o or down in Lon-don town a-go-
(2.) looked all o-ver the world and there's ev-'ry type of girl,

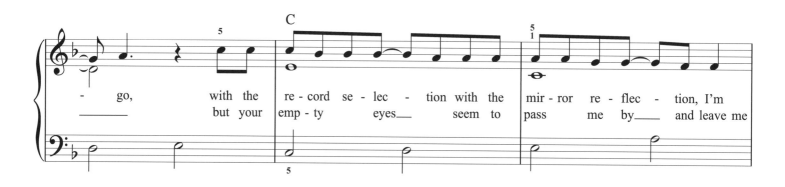

- go, with the re-cord se-lec-tion with the mir-ror re-flec-tion, I'm
_____ but your emp-ty eyes_____ seem to pass me by_____ and leave me

So let's

Fm   Fm(maj⁷)

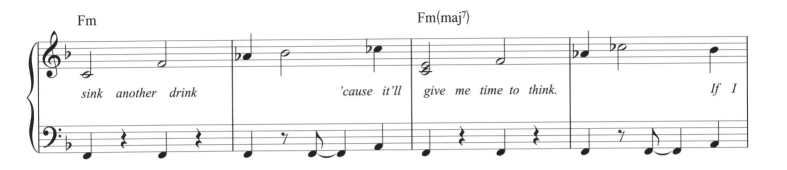

sink another drink   *'cause it'll*   *give me time to think.*   *If I*

Fm⁷   Fm(maj⁷)   Fm

had the chance   *I'd ask the world to dance.*   *And I'll be dancing with myself.*

         Fm(maj⁷)   Fm⁷

I'll be   *dancing with*   *myself.*

Fm(maj⁷)   N.C.

so let's sink another drink   *'cause it'll give me*   *time*   *to think.*

A - dim dom dah.___ A - dim dom

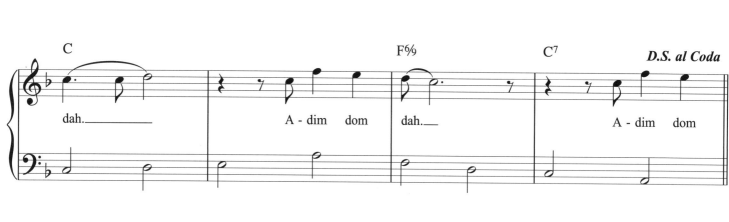

dah.___ A - dim dom dah.___ A - dim dom

D.S. al Coda

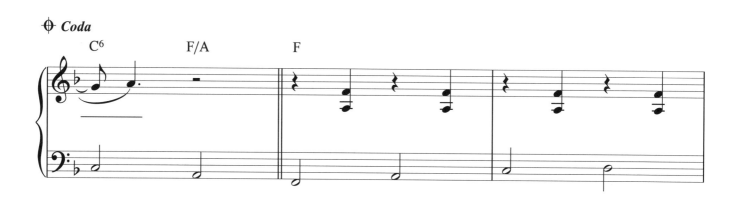

Coda

22

Defying Gravity

Words & Music by Stephen Schwartz

It's time to trust my in - stincts, close my eyes___ and leap.
Well, if that's love it comes___ at much too high___ a cost.

It's time___ to try de - fy - - ing
I'd soon - er buy, de - fy - - ing

gra - vi - ty. I think I'll try de - fy - - ing
gra - vi - ty. Kiss me good - bye, I'm de - fy - - ing

gra - vi - ty. Kiss me good - bye,___ I'm de - fy - - ing
gra - vi - ty. I think I'll try___ de - fy - - ing

1.

gra - vi - ty and you won't bring me down.
gra - vi - ty and you won't bring me

down. I'd soon- er

buy, de - fy - ing gra - vi - ty. Kiss me good -

- bye,_____ I'm de - fy - ing gra - vi - ty. I think I'll

try de - fy - ing gra - vi - ty. And you won't bring__ me

down. Bring me down. Oh!_____

Don't Stop Believin'

Words & Music by Steve Perry, Neal Schon & Jonathan Cain

1° only

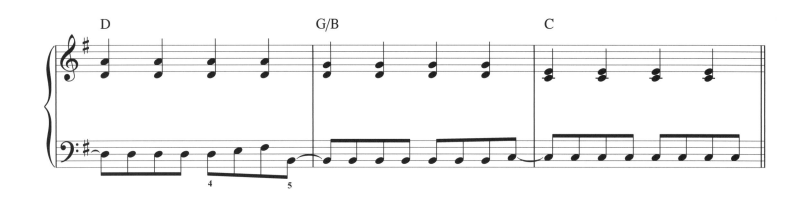

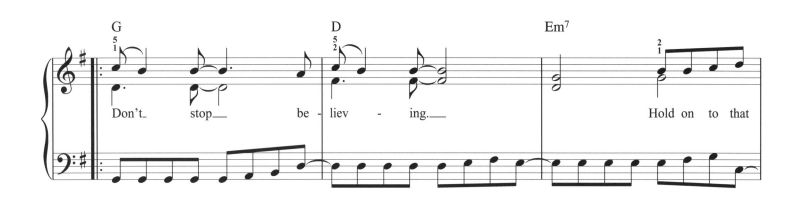

Don't__ stop__ be - liev - ing.__   Hold on to that

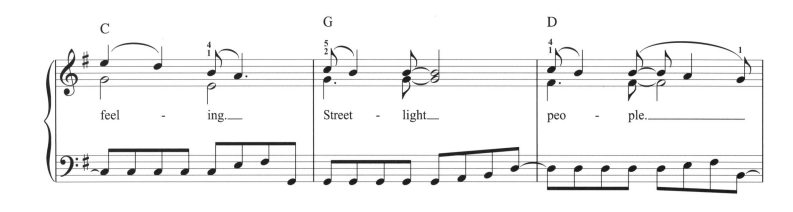

feel - ing.__   Street - light__   peo - ple._____

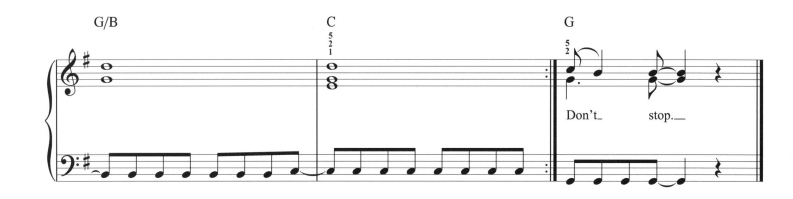

Don't__ stop.__

Imagine

Words & Music by John Lennon

it   is - n't   hard____   to   do.
I   won - der   if____   you   can.

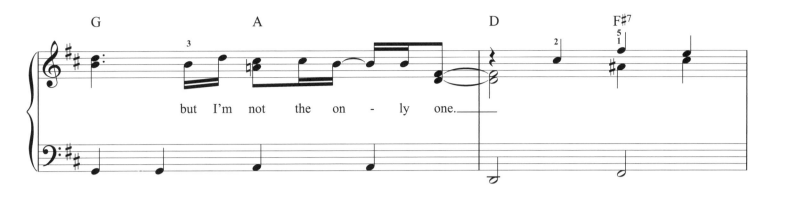

but I'm not the on - ly one._____

I hope some day_____ you will join us._____

1.

And the world_____ will be as one._____

2.

rit.

And the world_____ will live as one._____

Keep Holding On

Words & Music by Avril Lavigne & Lukasz Gottwald

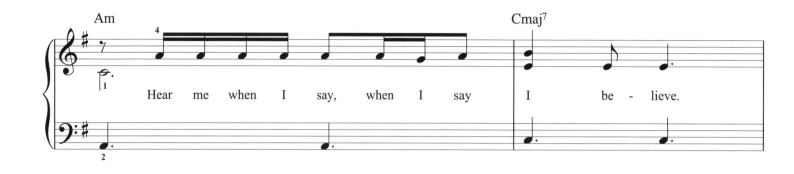

Am ... Cmaj⁷

Hear me when I say, when I say I be - lieve.

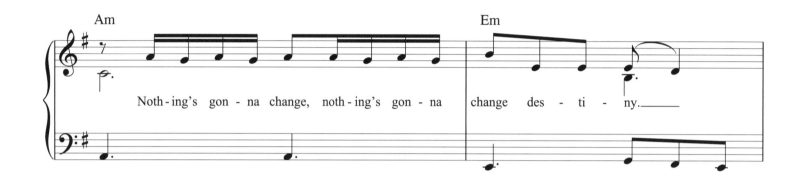

Am ... Em

Noth-ing's gon - na change, noth-ing's gon - na change des - ti - ny.___

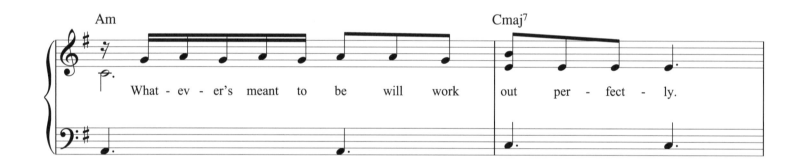

Am ... Cmaj⁷

What - ev - er's meant to be will work out per - fect - ly.

G

Yeah,___ yeah,___ yeah,___ yeah.___ La la la

Bm/F♯ ... Em⁷ ... Csus² ... *D.S. al Coda*

la la la la la la la la la la la la la la la.

Maybe This Time

Words by Fred Ebb
Music by John Kander

My Life Would Suck Without You

Words & Music by Max Martin, Lukasz Gottwald
& Claude Kelly

Lean On Me

Words & Music by Bill Withers

A E A
we know that there's always to-mor - row. Lean on me
D A A/E
when you're not strong and I'll be your friend I'll help you car-
E A D A
- ry on. For it won't be long till I'm gon-na need
E A D
some-bod-y to lean on. Please, swal-low your pride,
A A/E E A D
if I have things you need to bor - row. For no-one can fill

Sweet Caroline

Words & Music by Neil Diamond

Take A Bow

Words & Music by Mikkel Eriksen, Tor Erik Hermansen
& Shaffer Smith

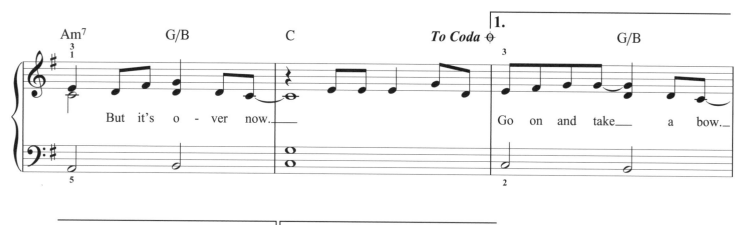

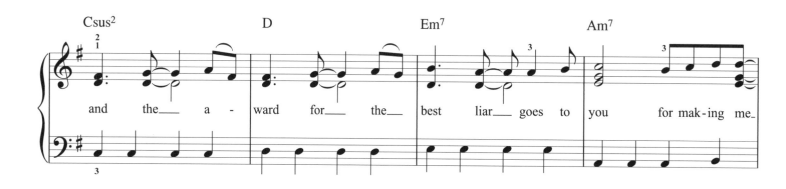

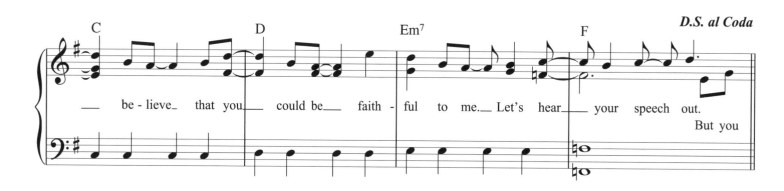

56

True Colours

Words & Music by Billy Steinberg & Tom Kelly

(You're) Having My Baby

Words & Music by Paul Anka